Carol, gaily carol

Christmas songs for children
chosen by Beatrice Harrop

Words edition

A & C Black Ltd · London

Contents

Mary and the angel, 1

The journey to Bethlehem, 3

Seeking a place to stay, 5

Round the crib, 9

Shepherds and kings, 27

Celebrating Christmas, 39

Index of first lines

A MUSIC EDITION is also available (with piano accompaniments, with chords for guitar, and with parts for descant recorders, glockenspiel, chime bars and percussion

Reprinted 1974
ISBN 0 7136 1406 4 (words) 0 7136 1407 2 (music spiral bound)
0 7136 1408 0 (music laminated boards)
Printed in Great Britain by
Hollen Street Press Ltd at Slough

1

1 Mary met an angel unexpectedly,
When she was a-walking in the garden.
Mary said, "Oh angel, how you startled me!"
When she was a-walking in the garden.

2 Mary was excited and fell on her knee,
When she met the angel in the garden.
Angel he said, "Mary, don't be scared of me,"
When she met that angel in the garden.

3 Angel promised Mary God would send a son,
As they stood there talking in the garden.
"When he comes," he said, "he'll be a special
one,"
As they stood there talking in the garden.

4 Angel disappeared unexpectedly;
Mary went on walking in the garden.
She thought, "It's quite marvellous that God
chose me,"
As she went on walking in the garden.

2

1 Now tell us, gentle Mary,
What did Gabriel say to you?
Now tell us of the tidings
That he brought to Galilee.
He told me I was favoured,
That I would be the one
God chose to be the mother
Of Jesus, his own son.

2 Now tell us, gentle Mary,
Of the birth of Christ that morn.
Now tell us of Christ Jesus,
Where it was that he was born.
Not in a palace glorious,
Not in a silken bed,
But in a stable humble
Did Jesus lay his head.

3

Little donkey, little donkey,
On the dusty road,
Got to keep on plodding onwards
With your precious load.
Been a long time, little donkey,
Through the winter's night.
Don't give up now, little donkey,
Bethlehem's in sight.

Ring out those bells tonight,
Bethlehem, Bethlehem.
Follow that star tonight,
Bethlehem, Bethlehem.
Little donkey, little donkey,
Had a heavy day.
Little donkey, carry Mary
Safely on her way.

Little donkey, carry Mary
Safely on her way.

4

1 Here we go up to Bethlehem,
Bethlehem, Bethlehem,
Here we go up to Bethlehem
On a cold and frosty morning.

2 We've got to be taxed in Bethlehem,
Bethlehem, Bethlehem,
We've got to be taxed in Bethlehem
On a cold and frosty morning.

3 Where shall we stay in Bethlehem,
Bethlehem, Bethlehem?
Where shall we stay in Bethlehem
On a cold and frosty morning?

5

1 Joseph is sad as he travels the way,
Mary is tired at the end of the day.
"Innkeeper, have you a room for us, pray?
May we stay here till the morning?"

2 Here in the stable the weary may rest.
Oxen and asses will welcome the guest,
He will be safe as a bird in its nest,
Jesus will come in the morning.

6

1 Lodging, I beg you, good man,
In the name of heaven!
My wife is weary;
She says she can go no farther.
Long have we travelled,
Have mercy on us, good man!
God will reward you
If you will give shelter to her.

2 There is no room in this place
For any stranger.
I do not know you;
Be gone, and all talking cease!
I do not care
If great distance you have come.
All of your pleading is vain,
So go away, let us have our peace.

7

Standing in the rain,
Knocking on the window,
Knocking on the window
On a Christmas Day.
There he is again,
Knocking on the window,
Knocking on the window
In the same old way.

1 No use knocking on the window.
There is nothing we can do, sir.
All the beds are booked already,
There is nothing left for you, sir.
Standing in the rain . . .

2 No, we haven't got a manger,
No, we haven't got a stable.
'Till you woke us with your knocking,
We were sleeping like the dead, sir.
Standing in the rain . . .

8

1 Rat-a-tat-tat, Rat-a-tat-tat,
No! No! No!
There isn't any room
And you can't stay here,
There isn't any room for strangers.
The wind may be chill
And the night may be cold,
And be full of nasty noises in the dark
 and dangers.
But there isn't any room,
 There isn't any room,
 There isn't any room for strangers.

2 Rat-a-tat-tat, Rat-a-tat-tat,
Yes! Yes! Yes!
There is a little room
And you may stay here,
We have a little place for strangers.
Come in from the night
To the stable so bare
Which is full of warmth and friendliness
 and safe from dangers.
Yes, there is a little room,
 There is a little room,
 There is a little room for strangers.

9

1 Baby Jesus, sleeping softly
On the warm and fragrant hay,
Children all the wide world over
Think of you on Christmas Day.

2 Mother Mary watching Jesus
Sleeping in the soft warm hay,
Children all the wide world over
Think of you on Christmas Day.

3 Joseph standing close beside them
Hearing what the shepherds say,
Children all the wide world over
Think of you on Christmas Day.

10

1 Come, see this little stranger
That lies all warm within;
His cradle is a manger,
His home a way-side inn;
Come, let us look within.

2 The breath of oxen warms him,
They watch this baby dear,
They see no chill shall harm him,
So long as they are near,
This little babe to cheer.

11

1 Come, they told me,
parum pum pum pum,
A new-born king to see,
parum pum pum pum,
Our finest gifts we bring,
parum pum pum pum,
To lay before the king,
parum pum pum pum,
rum pum pum pum, rum pum pum pum.
So to honour him,
parum pum pum pum,
When we come.

2 Baby Jesus . . .
I am a poor boy too . . .
I have no gift to bring . . .
That's fit to give our king . . .
Shall I play for you . . .
On my drum?

3 Mary nodded . . .
The ox and lamb kept time . . .
I played my drum for him . . .
I played my best for him . . .
Then he smiled at me . . .
Me and my drum.

12

1 Girls and boys, leave your toys,
make no noise,
Kneel at his crib and worship him.
At thy shrine, Child divine,
we are thine,
Our Saviour's here.
"Hallelujah" the church bells ring,
"Hallelujah" the angels sing,
"Hallelujah" from everything.
All must draw near.

2 On that day, far away,
Jesus lay,
Angels were watching round his head.
Holy child, mother mild,
undefiled,
We sing thy praise.
"Hallelujah" the church bells ring . . .

3 Shepherds came at the fame
of thy name,
Angels their guide to Bethlehem.
In that place, saw thy face
filled with grace,
Stood at thy door.
"Hallelujah" the church bells ring . . .

13

Hey, little bull behind the gate,
What are you doing up so late?
And, little bull, what have you seen
On this starry Christmas Eve?

1 If you raise your eyes to heaven
You will see the Virgin's Son,
He is clothed in white apparel
And is blessing everyone.

La-la la-la la la la la la
La la la la-la la-la la-la la
La-la la-la la la la la la
La la-la la la-la la la la.

2 Forward, forward, little shepherd,
March on bravely, everyone,
Thanking God with hearts o'erflowing
For the gift of his blessed son.

Hey, little bull behind the gate,
What are you doing up so late?
And, little bull, what have you seen
On this starry Christmas Eve?

14

1 Infant holy, infant lowly,
For his bed a cattle stall;
Oxen lowing, little knowing
Christ the babe is Lord of all.
Swift are winging angels singing,
Nowell's ringing, tidings bringing,
Christ the babe is Lord of all,
Christ the babe is Lord of all.

2 Flocks were sleeping, shepherds keeping
Vigil till the morning new,
Saw the glory, heard the story,
Tidings of a gospel true.
Thus rejoicing, free from sorrow,
Praises voicing, greet the morrow,
Christ the babe was born for you,
Christ the babe was born for you.

15

1 It was poor little Jesus,
Yes, Yes.
He was born on a Friday,
Yes, Yes.
Didn't have no cradle,
Yes, Yes.

Wasn't that a pity and a shame,
O Lord.
Wasn't that a pity and a shame.

2 It was poor little Jesus,
Yes, Yes.
The child of Mary,
Yes, Yes.
He was laid in a manger,
Yes, Yes.
Wasn't that a pity . . .

3 He was born on a Christmas,
Yes, Yes.
He was born on a Christmas,
Yes, Yes.
Didn't have no shelter,
Yes, Yes.
Wasn't that a pity . . .

16

Jesus, Jesus, rest your head,
You has got a manger bed.
All the evil folk on earth
Sleep in feathers at their birth.
Jesus, Jesus, rest your head,
You has got a manger bed.

1 Have you heard about our Jesus?
Have you heard about his fate?
How his mammy went to that stable
On that Christmas Eve so late?
Winds were blowing, cows were lowing,
Stars were glowing, glowing, glowing.
Jesus, Jesus, rest your head . . .

2 To that manger came the wise men,
Bringing things from hin and yon
For the mother and the father
And the blessed little son.
Milkmaids left their fields and flocks
And sat beside the ass and ox.
Jesus, Jesus, rest your head . . .

17

Jesus borned in Bethlea,
Jesus borned in Bethlea,
Jesus borned in Bethlea,
　　and in the manger lay.
And in the manger lay,
　　and in the manger lay,
Jesus borned in Bethlea,
　　and in the manger lay.

18

1 Jesus, our brother, kind and good,
Was humbly born in a stable rude;
And the friendly beasts around him stood,
Jesus, our brother, kind and good.

2 "I," said the donkey, shaggy and brown,
"I carried his mother up-hill and down,
I carried her safely to Bethlehem town."
"I," said the donkey, shaggy and brown.

3 "I," said the cow, all white and red,
"I gave him my manger for a bed,
I gave him my hay to pillow his head."
"I," said the cow, all white and red.

4 "I," said the sheep with the curly horn,
"I gave him my wool for a blanket warm,
He wore my coat on Christmas morn."
"I," said the sheep with the curly horn.

5 "I," said the dove from the rafters high,
"I cooed him to sleep so he would not cry,
We cooed him to sleep, my mate and I."
"I," said the dove from the rafters high.

Repeat the first verse

19

1 Lullaby, Jesus,
My dear one, be sleeping.
Lullaby, Jesus,
While watch I am keeping.

Lullaby, baby,
My darling, I love you.
Your mother will sing
And so gently will rock you.

2 When you awaken,
Sweet Jesus, I'll give you
Raisins and almonds
And sweet berries too.
Lullaby, baby . . .

3 Hush, he is sleeping
While stars shine above us;
Like the bright sun
Is the sweet baby Jesus.
Lullaby, baby . . .

20

1 A little child was born in a stall,
A little child was born in a stall.
He brought to the world much joy for us all,
He brought to the world much joy for us all.

2 Yes, God's own son in a manger lay,
Yes, God's own son in a manger lay.
He slept in a cradle of wood and of hay,
He slept in a cradle of wood and of hay.

21

1 Mary had a baby,
Yes, Lord.
Mary had a baby,
Yes, my Lord.
Mary had a baby,
Yes, Lord.
The people keep a-coming
And the train done gone.

2 What did she name him?
Yes, Lord . . .

3 Mary named him Jesus,
Yes, Lord . . .

4 Where was he born?
Yes, Lord . . .

5 Born in a stable,
Yes, Lord . . .

6 Where did Mary lay him?
Yes, Lord . . .

7 Laid him in a manger,
Yes, Lord . . .

22

1 Mary was watching tenderly
Her little son;
Softly the mother sang to sleep
Her darling one.
Sleep, lovely child, be now at rest,
Dear son of light;
Sleep, pretty fledgling, in your nest
All through the night.

2 Mary has spread your manger bed,
Sleep, little dove;
God's creatures all draw near to praise
And give their love.
Sleep little pearl, creator, Lord,
Our praises take;
Bees bring you honey from their hoard
When you awake.

23

1 O come, little children,
O come, one and all!
O come to the cradle
in Bethlehem's stall;
The bright star will guide us
and show us the way
To Jesus who's lying
asleep on the hay.

2 O come, everybody,
O come to the stall,
With hearts full of love
for this baby so small.
O sing, little children,
to him you adore;
O sing with the angels,
sing peace evermore!

24

1 Run with torches to light the dim stable,
Run with torches, good villagers, run!
Christ is born, O come and adore him;
Mary calls you; kneel before him.
Ah! Ah!
Beautiful mother Mary!
Ah! Ah!
Beautiful baby son!

2 Make no noise as you hurry to greet him,
Make no noise, no disturbance make!
One and all, as you come to adore him,
Quietly, quietly kneel before him;
Hush! Hush!
See, he is gently sleeping,
Hush! Hush!
Quietly lest he wake!

3 See who knocks on the door so loudly,
See who knocks, O good people, see!
"Open, please, that I may adore him;
Lay my plate of cakes before him;
Tock! Tock!
Merrily let me greet him.
Tock! Tock!
Merrily join with me."

25

1 Sleep quietly, my Jesus,
Now close your dear eyes.
Above you shine God's countless stars,
Like diamonds in the sky.
Beside your bed, a manger crude,
Where cattle have fed,
Your mother stands in watchful prayer
And strokes your little head.

2 The shepherds leave their flocks and come,
They bring you their love,
While angels of our Father God
Rejoice in song above.
From far away the wise men three
Their treasures do bring.
The whole wide world before you kneels,
My Jesus, little king.

26

1 What shall I give
To the child in the manger?
What shall I give
To the beautiful boy?
Grapes I will give to him,
Hanging in clusters,
Baskets of figs
For the child to enjoy.
Tam-pa-tam-tam
When the figs will have ripened,
Tam-pa-tam-tam
They will add to his joy.

2 What shall I give
To the child in the manger?
What shall I give
To the beautiful boy?
Garlands of flowers
To twine in his fingers,
Cherries so big
For the child to enjoy.
Tam-pa-tam-tam
When the cherries have ripened,
Tam-pa-tam-tam
They will add to his joy.

27

Go, tell it on the mountain,
Over the hills and everywhere,
Go, tell it on the mountain
That Jesus Christ is born.

1 While shepherds kept their watching
Over wandering flocks by night,
Behold from out of heaven
There shone a holy light.
Go, tell it on the mountain . . .

2 And lo, when they had seen it,
They all bowed down and prayed,
They travelled on together
To where the babe was laid.
Go, tell it on the mountain . . .

28

1 Andrew mine, Jasper mine,
Timothy and Abel,
Hurry to Bethlehem
To the common stable.
There you'll find a baby small,
Sleeping in a swaddling shawl,
On your way, on your way,
To our Saviour born today.

2 When you're there, bow in prayer,
In that stable thither,
Tribute pay while I play
On my well-tuned zither.
Lay beside him all your gifts,
Carried through the snow and drifts:
Ducks and geese, milk and cheese,
Kneel unto the Prince of Peace.

29

1 Melchior and Balthazar
Came from Africa,
Came from Africa;
Melchior and Balthazar
Came from Africa,
Oh yes, with King Gaspar!

2 When they came to Bethlehem,
They unpacked their hampers,
They unpacked their hampers;
When they came to Bethlehem,
They unpacked their hampers,
Oh yes, and their tents!

3 Like three starved and hungry wolves,
They ate all their soup,
They ate all their soup;
Like three starved and hungry wolves,
They ate all their soup,
And it was cabbage soup!

30

1 In a cold and dark December,
Fum, fum, fum,
In a cold and dark December,
Fum, fum, fum,
To the Virgin Mary mild
Was born a darling little child
With a message of salvation,
Raise a cry of jubilation,
Fum, fum, fum.

2 Shepherds left their flocks at midnight,
Fum, fum, fum,
Shepherds left their flocks at midnight,
Fum, fum, fum,
By the angels' tidings led
To seek the lowly manger bed,
Bowed down in adoration
To the child of their salvation,
Fum, fum, fum.

31

1 Lift up lightly the stable bar,
Weary wise men come from afar
Led by the little king's bright new star—
Is the little king sleeping?

2 Golden gifts for a baby king,
Cloth of gold and a golden ring,
Set by the cradle this gift I bring—
Is the little king sleeping?

3 Frankincense for a priest divine,
Born on this first Christmas time,
Set by the cradle this gift of mine—
Is the little king sleeping?

4 Myrrh for bitterness yet to be,
Let it not trouble his infancy.
—Hush, my companions, and pray with me—
Is the little king sleeping?

32

1 Oh, who would be a shepherd boy
And mind a flock of sheep,
While other men and boys enjoy
A quiet night of sleep?

2 Yes, who would choose to pass the night
In darkness and in cold?
Or hear the cry without a fright:
"A wolf is in the fold"?

3 Now then there came a shining one,
An angel of the Lord;
With news of God's eternal son,
By angels now adored.

4 "The news," said he, "should make you glad,
And fill your hearts with joy:
You'll find him in a manger laid,
A mother's baby boy."

5 The shepherds' hearts were comforted
By what was told to them.
"And after what we've heard," they said,
"Let's go to Bethlehem."

33

1 “Philip, awake, I pray!”
   “Why waken me?”
“Listen to what I say!”
   “O, let me be!”
“Come with me out in the night,
See what a wondrous sight,
Darkness is turned to light!”
   “How can that be?”

2 “Now I hear music too!”
   “I nothing hear.”
“Come, bring your pipe with you!”
   “I have it here.”
“Angels’ clear voices ring;
News of great joy they bring;
To us is born a king!”
   “What tidings rare!”

3 “Born in a cattle-shed!”
   “How do you know?”
“That’s what the angel said.”
   “Oh, did he so?”
“Pure is the maiden fair,
Mary, his mother dear.
See, the star shines so clear!”
   “Come, let us go!”

34

1 Shepherds have left their sheep,
Merrily ding-a-ding-a-dong,
All for a child asleep,
Joyful our song.
Low in the manger lies,
Merrily ding-a-ding-a-dong,
Lord of the starry skies,
Joyful our song.

2 Wise men have come to see,
Merrily ding-a-ding-a-dong,
Jesus on Mary's knee,
Joyful our song.
See the star shine for them,
Merrily ding-a-ding-a-dong,
High over Bethlehem,
Joyful our song.

3 Hark to the bells that ring
Merrily ding-a-ding-a-dong,
Jesus is born a king,
Joyful our song.
Bells in the air above,
Merrily ding-a-ding-a-dong,
Ringing of peace and joy,
Joyful our song.

35

1 Some wise men in their splendour
Were following the star.
It led them on their journey
From eastern lands afar,
It led them on their journey
From eastern lands afar.

2 That star led them to Bethl'em
Where Baby Jesus lay;
The new-born king was sleeping,
In borrowed bed of hay,
The new-born king was sleeping
In borrowed bed of hay.

3 For they had gifts to offer
Myrrh, frankincense and gold.
They gave them to the baby,
The Saviour long foretold,
They gave them to the baby,
The Saviour long foretold.

36

1 There were three kings
A journey did go,
Led by a star
Through the cold winter's snow.
Joyfully they came on their way,
A-searching for him
Who was born on that day.
With drums and with trumpets
They came on their way,
With drums and with trumpets
They came on their way.

2 An angel came,
To Joseph did say,
"Oh, hurry to Egypt!
Go! Please don't delay!
Herod comes near, vengeance to reap,
So hurry now, hasten,
And, Mary, don't weep!"
On donkey they went
With sweet Jesus asleep!
Held closely by Mary,
Sweet Jesus did sleep.

37

1 Winds through the olive trees
Softly did blow
Round little Bethlehem,
Long, long ago.

2 Sheep on the hillside lay
White as the snow;
Shepherds were watching them,
Long, long ago.

3 Then from the happy skies
Angels bent low,
Singing their songs of joy,
Long, long ago.

4 For in his manger bed
Cradled we know,
Christ came to Bethlehem,
Long, long ago.

38

1 Under Bethlehem's star so bright,
Shepherds watched their flocks by night.

Hydom, hydom, tidlidom,
Hydom, hydom, tidlidom.

2 Came an angel telling them
They must go to Bethlehem.
Hydom, hydom . . .

3 "Hasten, hasten," they did say,
"Jesus Christ you'll find that way."
Hydom, hydom . . .

4 "Sleeping in a manger bare
Lies the holy child so fair."
Hydom, hydom . . .

5 "Mary rocks him tenderly,
Joseph sings a lullaby."
Hydom, hydom . . .

39

1 Now light one thousand Christmas lights
On dark earth here tonight;
One thousand, thousand also shine
To make the dark sky bright.

2 Oh, once when skies were starry bright,
In stable cold and bare,
Sweet Mary bore a son that night,
A child both kind and fair.

3 She named her little son Jesu,
Sweet Mary, meek and mild,
She cradled and she rocked him too,
That little tiny child.

4 He came to bring us love and light,
To bring us peace on earth,
So let your candles shine tonight,
And sing with joy and mirth.

5 Now light one thousand Christmas lights
On dark earth here tonight;
One thousand, thousand also shine
To make the dark sky bright.

40

Blow the trumpet and bang the drum,
Set all the bells in the steeple ringing,
Blow the trumpet and bang the drum,
Tell the world that the Boy has come.

1 Through four thousand years of night,
There were priests and prophets singing,
Through four thousand years of night,
"He will come with the morning light."
Blow the trumpet and bang the drum . . .

2 O how charming, O how gay,
All our hearts with his sweetness winning,
O how charming, O how gay,
Christ the Boy in his cradle lay!
Blow the trumpet and bang the drum . . .

3 Boy and king we kneel before,
While the bells in the sky are ringing,
Boy and king we kneel before,
Be our ruler for evermore.
Blow the trumpet and bang the drum . . .

41

1 O Christmas tree, O Christmas tree,
How lovely are your branches.
O Christmas tree, O Christmas tree,
How lovely are your branches.
In beauty green they'll always grow
Through summer sun and winter snow.
O Christmas tree, O Christmas tree,
How lovely are your branches.

2 O Christmas tree, O Christmas tree,
You are the tree most loved.
O Christmas tree, O Christmas tree,
You are the tree most loved.
How often you give us delight
In brightly shining Christmas light!
O Christmas tree, O Christmas tree,
You are the tree most loved.

3 O Christmas tree, O Christmas tree,
Your beauty green will teach me,
O Christmas tree, O Christmas tree,
Your beauty green will teach me.
That hope and love will ever be
The way to joy and peace for me.
O Christmas tree, O Christmas tree,
Your beauty green will teach me.

42

The first day of Christmas
My true love sent to me
        A partridge in a pear tree
The second day . . .
        Two turtle doves
The third day . . .
        Three French hens
The fourth day . . .
        Four coloured birds
The fifth day . . .
        Five gold rings
The sixth day . . .
        Six geese a-laying
The seventh day . . .
        Seven swans a-swimming
The eighth day . . .
        Eight maids a-milking
The ninth day . . .
        Nine drummers drumming
The tenth day . . .
        Ten pipers piping
The eleventh day . . .
        Eleven ladies dancing
The twelfth day . . .
        Twelve lords a-leaping

43

1 We wish you a Merry Christmas,
We wish you a Merry Christmas,
We wish you a Merry Christmas
And a Happy New Year.

Good tidings we bring
To you and your kin;
We wish you a Merry Christmas
And a Happy New Year.

2 Now bring us some figgy pudding (3 times)
And bring some out here.
Good tidings we bring . . .

3 For we all like figgy pudding (3 times)
So bring some out here.
Good tidings we bring . . .

4 And we won't go until we've got some (3 times)
So bring some out here.
Good tidings we bring . . .

Acknowledgements

Grateful acknowledgement is made to Peggy Blakeley, Pat Lloyd—Deputy Head of Great Staughton County Primary School and Mary Collins—Head of Grange County Infant School, Gosport, Hampshire for help in compiling this selection of carols. Carols 1 and 8 have been specially written for this book by Peggy Blakeley. The cover design is by C. R. Evans.

The following have kindly granted their permission for the reprinting of carols which are their copyright:
Blandford Press Ltd. and Schmitt, Hall and McCreary Company, U.S.A. for 2—"Now tell us, gentle Mary", 6—"Lodging, I beg you, good man" and 25—"Sleep quietly, my Jesus" from *Carols of the Nations* compiled by Ruth Heller.
Bregman, Vocco and Conn Limited for 11—"Come, they told me" (The Little Drummer Boy) by Katherine Davis.
Chappell & Co. Ltd. for 3—"Little Donkey" by Eric Boswell. © 1959 Chappell & Co. Ltd.
The Czechoslovak Red Cross for 22—"Mary was watching tenderly" and 38—"Under Bethlehem's star so bright".
Essex Music Group for 7—"Standing in the rain" by Sydney Carter and 15—"It was poor little Jesus".
Evans Bros. Ltd. for 5—"Joseph is sad" by E. M. Ponting from *Songs for the School Assembly*, edited by Percy M. Young and 14—"Infant holy, infant lowly" by E. M. G. Reed from *The Kingsway Carol Book*.
Faber Music Ltd. on behalf of the publishers J. Curwen & Sons Ltd. for 24—"Run with torches to light the dim stable" and 33—"Philip, awake, I pray" from *20 European Carols* by Mary Barham Johnson.
Galliard Ltd. for 4—"Here we go up to Bethlehem" by Sydney Carter.
The editor of *The Orange Carol Book* (1962) for 40—"Blow the trumpet and bang the drum" by Sydney Carter.
Lord Maybray-King for 31—"Lift up lightly the stable bar".
Oxford University Press for 10—"Come, see this little stranger" by Steuart Wilson, 12—"Girls and boys, leave your toys" (Zither Carol) by Malcolm Sargent, 13—"Hey, little bull behind the gate" by A. H. Green and 28—"Andrew mine, Jasper mine" by C. K. Offer.
The Religious Education Press, a member of the Pergamon Group, for the words and music of 9—"Baby Jesus, sleeping softly" from *The Nursery Song and Picture Book* (1947) by W. E. Barnard.
Roberton Publications (for J. Curwen & Sons Ltd.) for 30—"In a cold and dark December" (Fum, fum, fum) from *Three Spanish Carols*.
G. Schirmer for 16—"Jesus, Jesus, rest your head" from *10 Christmas Carols* and 26—"What shall I give to the child in the manger" from *A Christmas Carol Pageant* by A. Diller and K. S. Page.
Weidenfeld (Publishers) Ltd. for 19—"Lullaby, Jesus", 23—"O come, little children", 29—"Melchior and Balthazar", 32—"Oh, who would be a shepherd boy", 36—"There were three kings", 39—"Now light one thousand Christmas lights" and 41—"O Christmas Tree" from *A Book of Christmas Carols* by Haig and Regina Shekerjian.
June Witham for 35—"Some wise men in their splendour".
Carol 20—"A little child was born in a stall" is from *Songs for Today K-1* published by the Waterloo Music Company Limited, Waterloo, Ontario, Canada.

Every effort has been made to trace copyright owners but should any acknowledgement of rights have been omitted, this will be rectified in subsequent editions on notification being received by the publishers.

Index of first lines

A little child was born in a stall, 20
Andrew mine, Jasper mine, 28

Baby Jesus, sleeping softly, 9
Blow the trumpet and bang the drum, 40

Come, see this little stranger, 10
Come, they told me, parum-pum-pum-pum, 11

Girls and boys, leave your toys, 12
Go, tell it on the mountain, 27

Here we go up to Bethlehem, 4
Hey, little bull behind the gate, 13

In a cold and dark December, 30
Infant holy, infant lowly, 14
It was poor little Jesus, 15

Jesus borned in Bethlea, 17
Jesus, Jesus, rest your head, 16
Jesus, our brother, kind and good, 18
Joseph is sad as he travels the way, 5

Lift up lightly the stable bar, 31
Little donkey, little donkey, 3
Lodging, I beg you, good man, 6
Lullaby Jesus, 19

Mary had a baby, 21
Mary met an angel unexpectedly, 1
Mary was watching tenderly, 22
Melchior and Balthazar, 29

Now light one thousand Christmas lights, 39
Now tell us, gentle Mary, 2

O come, little children, 23
O Christmas tree, O Christmas tree, 41
Oh, who would be a shepherd boy, 32

Philip, awake, I pray, 33

Rat-a-tat-tat, Rat-a-tat-tat, 8
Run with torches to light the dim stable, 24

Shepherds have left their sheep, 34
Sleep quietly, my Jesus, 25
Some wise men in their splendour, 35
Standing in the rain, 7

The first day of Christmas, 42
There were three kings, 36

Under Bethlehem's star so bright, 38

We wish you a Merry Christmas, 43
What shall I give to the child in the manger, 26
Winds through the olive trees, 37